HOW
DOES IT FEEL?

HOW
DOES IT FEEL?

and other poems

DAVID SCOTT

Illustrated by Alan Marks

BLACKIE

Text copyright © 1989 David Scott
Illustrations © 1989 Alan Marks
First published 1989 by Blackie and Son Ltd

British Library Cataloguing in Publication Data

Scott, David, *1945*–
How does it feel
    I. Title II. Marks, Alan
    821'.914

    ISBN 0–216–92656–4

Typeset by Jamesway Graphics
Middleton, Manchester M24 2HD

Blackie and Son Ltd
7 Leicester Place
London WC2H 7BP

Printed in Great Britain

Introduction

Two moments of great excitement helped me to make a friend of poetry. Someone taught me a funny rhyme which is still about the only one I can recite by heart, and I wrote it down in the back of my Letts' School-Boys' Diary for 1955 under Notes. Here it is, spelling mistakes, ragged line order, and all:

> There was a man who had
> two sons
> and these two sons were
> brothers
> Tabious was the name of one
> and Tabackious was the other.
> Now these 2 sons
> they brought a pig they
> bought a pig on Monday.
> Tibyus fed it
> all the week Tabackius on
> the Sunday.
> Now these 2 sons
> they died at last they
> died of eating jelly
> Tabyus died upon
> his back
> Tabackius on his belly.

I loved the rhyme of 'jelly' with 'belly', and the mysterious, unspellable names 'Tabious' and 'Tabackius'.

Underneath this poem in the Notes page of the diary is a list of plants, and a diagram of where they were going to go in my small allotment behind the school woodwork shed. I wrote them as I heard them which is why the spelling is strange: cosma, nomesia, snaps, pansy, iris, mesobranthians, marigold, asters, clarkia. The names were as important as the plants, few of which grew. Words had a magic buried within them.

The second occasion of excitement came when I realized that poetry could be about how *I* felt. For a long while the world presented a rather remote face: history, maths, other people, foreign countries. What a breakthrough when I read a poem and realized that there was another person who had felt what I had felt. They had gone through the same experience and passed it on in word and rhythm. The world ceased to be remote. It became something you could receive messages from, or crack open and discover was alive. It had meaning, and a meaning which you could feel.

So now, when it comes to writing a book of poems for younger readers, that world of feelings is the one I want to share. I hope that when you read these poems, whatever your age, you will recognise similar experiences of your own.

David Scott

*To the children
of the three schools of my parishes:
Allhallows, Blennerhasset and
St Michael's, Bothel*

How Does it Feel?

How does it feel?
OK All right.
How does it really feel?
OK All right.
But how does it really, really feel
without saying OK?

Yesterday my kitten died
and the oceans of my eyes
burst wide open. How's that?

The Beginnings

When did I begin to feel,
O Mother dear, O Mother dear,
When did I begin to feel?

When I climbed into your bed,
O Mother dear,
and when long-suffering Dad said,
'I'll be off and leave him here.'

Dad sent packing to my room
stubbed his toe in the midnight gloom,
wrapped his knobbly knees around
my bunk, ten inches from the ground,
where the crumpled plastic sheet
didn't seem to hold the heat.

And I felt warm,
And felt no fear,
And your soft arm,
O Mother dear.

Where Do Feelings Come From?

Where do feelings come from?
They well up from within.
But where is this well inside us
and can you drop things in?

You can drop things in all right,
you can drop in shouts and blows
and you can drop in hate and fear
and tears will overflow.

But if you drop in love and peace
and kindness to the cat,
then you will draw out happiness
and that's a fact.

A Dinky Toy's Week

First day

Out of the box like out of a garage
shining red enamel
smooth on the carpet, zing
under the sofa.

Second day

under the sofa

Third day

hoovered out

Fourth day

up and down the garage lift
meeting other toys:
buses, sports cars, saloons,
lorries, tractors.
A few crashes.

Fifth day

upside down

Sixth day

lead bitten
rubber tyres chewed off
tongue forced through their tight loop
finger right through
knuckle caught in passenger window.

Seventh day

in a pocket
with sweet papers
and screwed-up handkerchief.

Grandma Says

Sometimes we get to talking about war
and Grandma says,
'There never used to be so much fighting.'

And when we talk about the awful weather
Grandpa says,
'It never used to be as bad as this.
The sun shone all the time
when I was a lad.'

I say, 'I'm just going to get the bus into town.'
and they say,
'There never used to be
writing all over the bus shelter.'

I say,
'There weren't many people in church yesterday,'
and Grandma says,
'I used to go three times every Sunday
when I was a girl
and walk two miles there and back.'

I told them I could hold my breath
for fifteen seconds under water
and it's really good fun.
Grandma says,
'I never used to breathe when I was a child,
my dear, it just wasn't done.'

Haunted House

No one has been in this garden
for a long time. 'Overgrown'
is not the word. There is the house,
conservatory, curtainless windows,
Estate Agent's board.
Summer fills the garden,
roasts the laurel leaves.
I should not be here,
but the emptiness draws me,
and the bees' drowsing hum
and the derelict lettuce frames.

16

A sash-window chinked open
is my chance to get inside.
Books have warned me of the burglar's
footprint in the flower-bed
so I lean to the window sill,
raise the window onto a dust filled sunbeam
and a pile of rags in the corner,
which has one eye a bearded face
and . . . oh . . . moves and shouts 'WHAT . . .'

and I am out of that
window and across the lawn
and into the bushes and
over the fence and back down the lane
faster than I've ever run in my life.

Birthday

The really good thing
about it being my birthday
is that if I get into trouble
I won't get punished.

People are kind to you on your birthday.
They forget how horrible you are
on every other day of the year,
when there's no excuse for them to be kind.

For one day, you are 'it'.
You are the tops.
You get the kisses. You are
knee-deep in wrapping paper.

You are a new number.
It is the day
before you have to write down
thank you ten times.

You can spill the lemonade
and Dad will say, 'I'm
always doing that.
Never mind, this time.'

Picking Up Something Alive

This is something quite other.
As I go to pick it up
all beating heart against
a thin fur chest. It cannot
decrease any more.
It is as small as a fledgling
in the corner can be.
I am surprised at its warmth:
its heart, its terrified stillness,
and my quite otherness to it.
It does not yet know
my desire to look after it:
to find the necessary bugs,
and the ear drop tube for water,
and the shoe-box home.
If it will have faith
soon I will hold it out
with a slight lift
for a launch.

'Sort of ' (Crunkle Crunch Slurp)

My brother always tries
to tell stories at breakfast.
They are usually very complicated
and we get lost in the first sentence.
'It was like this you see,'
(munch, crunch, slurp)
'this man,' (munch, crunch, slurp)
'lived in a castle and
there was this other man,'
(munch, crunch) 'who lived
in another sort of castle altogether.'

20

By this time my brother is into the toast
and spreading it badly all over the place,
'and the first man, you see,
sort of ' (crackle, crunch, drop) 'eurgh!'
'didn't like the other man, who lived,'
(wipe, wipe, smear) 'well, it wasn't actually
in a sort of castle, more of a,'
(crunkle, crunch)
'Oh, I've got marmite all over my track suit!'
Mum says, 'I told you you would.'
'And the first man got into a sort of helicopter,
though it wasn't really a . . .'
By this time, he is talking to himself.
Everyone else has disappeared,
to the loo, or cleaning their teeth.
'helicopter, it was a really weird,'
(crunkle, crunch, slurp).

The Hard Book

This is a hard book
in small print
with no pictures
and four columns on each page.

Every four lines or so
there is a number by the side
and for some reason some
words are in *italics*.

At the beginning of the book
there is a letter from
King James the First
especially to me, but

I must apologise
I have never read it.
It is too long, and, well,
doesn't look interesting.

It is the oldest book
I've ever touched,
and for some reason
I keep going back to it;

not to read you understand
just to turn the pages
catching the odd word
that's been dead for ages:

Melchizedek,
Og, Habbakuk, Nebuchadnezzar,
forever and ever amen.

'Crucify Him!'

This picture in my book
is one I often look at.
The sky is getting dark
and the Roman soldier's sleeping.

It's sad that someone kind
should get the others' blame,
and so few clothes left
and your mother weeping.

'What can I do to help?'
I can't get into the picture.
I can't untie you.
Will feeling sad be sufficient?

24

Stealing into the Roman Catholic Church

There is no one else in here at all.
No one to remind me I am small.
Nothing to stop me hear my heart.
Nothing to make me play a part.
Every other church I've been in
It's been cleaning day or singing.
This is empty, silent, cool.
This is not at all like school.

Server

No one else in my class
is a server.
There's no one to boast to
about it,
It's not quite the thing
I mention
when the talk's about girls
or football.
So I keep the language
to myself
and turn it over
on my tongue
and quietly leave the house
at half-past-six
when the other lads
are draping the newspapers
over themselves.

I light the candles
carry the missal
wash the priest's fingers
kneel without sniffing
through the Prayer of Consecration
to the blessing. Then I snuff
the candles watching
the smoke billow up
before remembering that
it will soon be school
where no one else in my class
is a server.

Big Words

I like big words
it doesn't matter what they mean.
The bigger they are the better,
the biggest you've ever seen.

I search them out
in dictionaries and atlases
and backs of cereal packets
and then a lot of practice

to get my tongue round
Popocatepetl
or my nose round Kanchenjunga
or my mouth round malinger
or my teeth round spittle.

Hands Together. Eyes closed.

What am I meant to feel
when I shut my eyes and pray?
Am I meant to see those stars
like in the Milky Way.

And should I feel my eyeballs
tumble through my head
or should I open them a chink
and see the world instead?

Yes, I will open them a chink
and see the world instead
and let that fill the empty space
that's all inside my head.

Angel

This coat feels funny.
These shoes are too tight.
I can't eat my breakfast,
I'd rather have a fight.

Why should I put my socks on
Or do my safety-belt?
Why can't I just see what's on
Or let the ice-cream melt?

Velcro is much easier.
Football's best inside.
I really can't stop teasing her.
Yes, of course I've tried.

Clothes look better scattered
Vests are warm in bed.
I didn't think it mattered
That I hit her on the head.

I really hate you Daddy
Until it's Christmas Eve
And then because it's Christmas
I'll really try to please.

Shylock

'If you prick me, do I not bleed.'

If I feel it
perhaps others feel it too.
I don't like being hit
and nor do you.

What Shylock said
is true
both for the Christian
and the Jew.

If we would want
to know how others feel
ask yourself
what things appeal
and what do not.

My Optical Illusion Book

1
Press your arm tight
against a wall,
for a minute.
(It might hurt).
Then stand back.
It will rise up,
like a drawbridge,
without you doing anything at all.

2
Off at last!
Beating the other train out.
The gradual gathering
of speed out of the station,
until you are staring
at the beach ball poster
on the next platform,
stiller than ever.

3
I have strained my eyes
silly, staring at vertical lines
which wobble, and shapes
that tell you
one thing one way and
another thing another way.
Close your eyes. Open them.
What's it look like now?

4
Q   So what, old bean?
A   So this. Things ain't always what they seem.

5
or the one where
you get hold of the book
and circle it round
like a loony,
until the wheels
set off on their owny.

6
Take any word
and say it a hundred times.
It'll sound absurd
and like something else
altogether, and the letters
will eat their tail:
Ginger Ale, Ginger rail, ginger
Railginger, railGinger, 'Rail! Ginger!'

Conclusion (or Moral)

But what if, say
even the most important bit
of truth, is just a blink away
from being its absolute opposite?

Raiding the Piggy Bank

There was always some good reason
for raiding the Piggy Bank.
Sweets generally. And no sooner
was the money in
than out came the knife,
up went the Piggy in the air
artfully pierced in the back,
so that the coin could be tipped
onto the blade and slid
down the shaft into
what was left of a waiting
cupped edge of hand.
Usually a superb catch.
But the more I got out
the less there seemed to be in
until the day that it
didn't seem worth bothering
not even for sweets.

Wonderful Uncle Reg

Uncle Reg says he's keeping his eyes skinned,
and then asks me to give him a hand.
He hasn't a leg to stand on,
and claims he's a one-man band.

His shoulder is one you can cry on
and his heart is a heart of gold.
His nose is kept on the grindstone,
and he's a thousand and one years old,

He's a dab hand at baking and cooking
getting better each time he tries.
He greases the pan with his elbows,
and makes cakes with the whites of his eyes.

Uncle Reg's Attic

Over there was the stuffed gorilla
red beads for its eyes, and the mange,
Pith helmet and trunk and mantilla,
— a thousand and one things that were strange.

A lily growing out of a gramophone,
animals that walked to the ark,
the foot of a ginormous elephant,
and the xylophone teeth of a shark.

The circular track of a railway,
the golf clubs and gas mask and screen,
a snap of Aunt Dot in her hey-day,
with a hat and a romantic lean.

'Mah-jongg' that he said I could master
if only there was the time.
The bust of Napoleon, in plaster,
and green paperback books about crime.

I loved Uncle Reg's attic
stuffed with the things that he'd found.
Aunt Dot used the word 'eccentric',
as he followed the trains round and round.

My School Bag

is like no one else's school bag.
It's a 'grip': two handles held together,
a zip (never done up) and four studs
on the bottom to give it that clunk
as it hits the floor at the beginning of lessons.

If it's left in the middle
of the playground, everyone would know
whose it was and say
'That's old banana face's,'
or something ruder.

Colour: canvas, light beige;
leather, dark beige,
but dirty all over, bashed about,
'well used,' you might say.

But it is nothing
compared with Mr T's:
which is so big and heavy
he swings it onto the desk
like as if he was lifting a mallet,
and out will come:
exercise books, games shirt,
socks, sandwiches, newspaper,
mark book, umbrella, hat, coat,
and if you're lucky, a bag of sweets.

Preparing for the Fairies

Could this be a loose tooth
I'm straining the hamstrings of my tongue
to dislodge. All day,
in and out of the crater
until hanging on by a single thread,
I knew its time was near.
The fairies were hovering to hear
the news, and in the depths of a carefully
wrapped–round
handkerchief, the small blood stained ivory,
worth 10p, 30p and some even get a £1.

First Girlfriend

Would she ever come to stay
again, and could I say
good–night, and would she promise
faithfully to marry me one day.

I loved her differently
from how I loved my mum.
There was an air of secrecy
about this one.

Something special happened
when we went through
the album with that photo
and there was us two
me in my shorts and jerkin, and oh!
you in your royal princess coat.

My Mirror is a Spoon

Before I eat my pudding
I look into my spoon.
Concave I feature upside down,
and convex like a loon.

Letter to a Car Thief

You can take the cassette player
You can take the leopard skin seats
You can take the switch on fresh air,
but leave me my travelsick sweets.

You can take the bonnet, the boot and the brakes,
and the heater that overheats.
You can take the exhaust and the noise that it makes
but leave me my travelsick sweets.

There's just one thing on which I stick
when offering our car to you cheats,
(unless you want everything covered in . . .)
and that's the travelsick sweets.

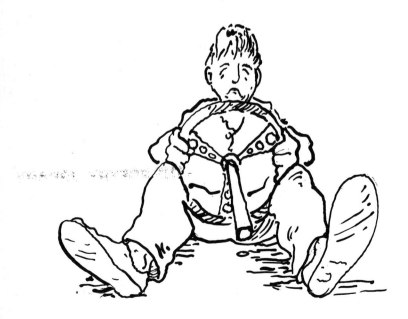

What Must It Be to Be Someone Else?

However hard it is being me
not to be me is harder.

I'd really like to be like you
riding on the handlebars.

I'd really like to be like you
sitting in my racing car,

but all the time is taken up
in trying to be me.

It never seems so daring,
it never seems so bright,
but deep down in my heart of hearts,
I know being me is right.

Giggling

The quieter it is the worse it becomes:
churches, concerts, when we have
to be quiet because someone's cross
because we've been too noisy over Sunday lunch.
Or one night at a concert in church
when we had to be quiet for a long time
and the lady in front had on a yellow sou'wester hat
and in the middle of the Mozart
I had this picture of a pilchard advertisement.
It was like a sneeze which I couldn't hold back.
I bit my lip, held my breath, did
heavy breathing, thought of something sad,
pretended to cry. What I would have given
for a mile of beach to laugh myself silly along.

Things That I Shouldn't Have Done

Things that I do that I shouldn't
are things that I shouldn't have done,
and the things that I haven't but I ought to
are the things that I ought to have done.
But things that I shouldn't and oughtn't
are things I wouldn't have done
if the should and the would had been easier
and the should not had not been such fun.

High Up

This is the highest I've ever been.
So high up I cannot be seen.
If I fall down I will surely die.
O why, o why did I climb so high?

Shoe Shop

The assistant takes off my
old shoes with the frayed laces
and the generally beaten-up look
which fitted perfectly. She says
how nice the new pair look,
which are stiff, too bright, and
cut me under the ankle bone.
Besides thay are laced in a different way
so you get one very long end
and one too short.
'Walk over there in them.'
They are like Eskimo snow shoes.
'Fine,' she says. 'Would you like to keep them on?'
as she buries my old pair
in tissue paper and a cardboard box.

Best Friend

Of those who could beat my head in
there is one I know who would not.
He it is who shares his sweets
and would never scoff the lot.

If he is captain of a team
he'll pick me though I'm bad.
He'll cover up my great own goal
and in cricket blame the pads.

Through all the battles of the day
I am his piggyback rider.
I tell him anything I may
like when I had too much cider.

He is big and I am small.
It doesn't make a difference.
It's something else that matters more,
the spark that moves between us.

Diving In

That he could dive in
with his arms by his side
kamikaze-bomber-style
was the greatest thing I'd
ever seen. That was what
I wanted to do. To find
my spear head parting the water
and my pointed feet zipping it up behind.
It eclipsed all other ambitions:
parachutist, man on the moon.
I just wanted that precision
and daring, to be like the one
I had seen be a dolphin.

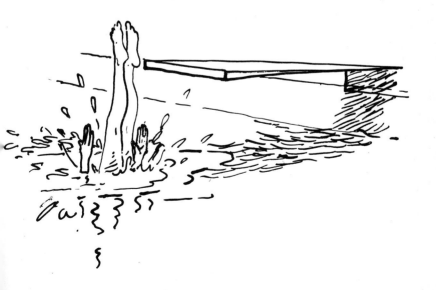

Eating at School

This ham fat staring at me
is not going to be eaten in a hurry.
First I will cut it into twenty pieces
accidentally spilling some on the floor
and some behind the radiator. Making sure
the glass of water is full. I shall take
each of the dreaded squares,
fill my mouth with water
and swilling both round
attempt to swallow the fat, that
I know I ought to eat, but can't, can't.
'Won't, more like,' says the commandant.
I choose the smallest of the squares
(the one with a bit of lean on it)
put it in, grab the glass, drink the water, and
alas, gag. I undo my collar button.
Of the pieces, that was just the first one.

Climbing a Mountain

There is the first top
and then there is another
and then quite a lot of
heather and rock
and you're still not at the top.
You wonder if you'll ever make it
and stop, just for a bit,
to see where you've come from
and the view of the Isle of Man;
the cotton thread of river in the valley,
cars like ants. 'Will it
ever be the top?' You say to the
three black crows, the buzzard,
and the ever so sprightly
(because it lives here) pipit.
They say, 'Keep on, keep on,'
as does the group, for whom,
for fear of being left behind,
I summon all my energy.
And then the cries of 'Top!
This is the top!' (Not Everest.
But the best yet, and the moment
for the chocolate.)

Accidents Happen, But I Wish They Didn't

You can be laughing and joking
one minute, and then
the next, you've caught your finger in the door;
and you can't remember that
there was anything called 'before'.
And all day long
it's 'the day you caught your finger in the door.'

Bricks

The big difference between us
is that you want to build the house up
and I want to knock the house down.
So you'll have to be quick
because as soon as that last brick
is placed on the very, very leaning top,
I'm going to give the whole thing a tremendous
wallop,
and there'll be bricks flying everywhere.
'Don't you dare!'
(Wallop). Brick bombs. Brick rain.
(Long silence)
'Can you build it again?'

Feeling Floaty

I feel frightened in my tummy.
I feel clever in my head.
I feel brave when I'm with Mummy,
but tell me,
will it be floaty when I'm dead?

Some Days

Some days I feel nothing,
and nothing feels me.
It wraps me up in a blanket
on the sitting-room settee.

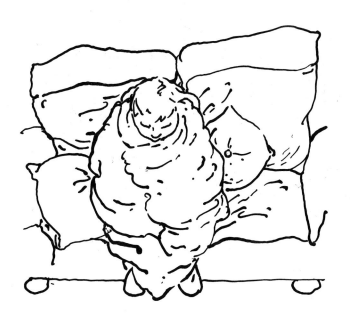

Index of First Lines

Before I eat my pudding 41
Could this be a loose tooth 39
First day 12
How does it feel 9
However hard it is being me 43
I feel frightened in my tummy 54
I like big words 28
If you prick me, do I not bleed 31
Is like no one else's school bag. 38
My brother always tries 20
No one else in my class 26
No one has been in this garden 16
Of those who could beat my head in 48
Over there was the stuffed gorilla 36
Press your arm tight 32
Some days I feel nothing 55
Sometimes we get to talking about War 14
That he could dive in 49
The assistant takes off my 47
The big difference between us 53
The quieter it is the worse it becomes 44
The really good thing 18
There is no one else in here at all 25
There is the first top 51
There was always some good reason 34
Things that I do that I shouldn't 45
This coat feels funny 30
This ham fat staring at me 50
This is a hard book 22
This is something quite other 19
This is the highest I've ever been 46
This picture in my book 24
Uncle Reg says he's keeping his eyes skinned 35
What am I meant to feel 29
When did I begin to feel 10
Where do feelings come from 11
Would she ever come to stay 40
You can be laughing and joking 52
You can take the cassette player 42